THE
DATA
ESCALATOR

Helen Tanner

The Data Escalator

Copyright Helen Tanner © 2020

ISBN 978-1-91313-09-6

First Published by Compass-Publishing 2020
www.compass-publishing.com

Printed in the United Kingdom

A catalogue version of the book can be found at the British Library

Designed by The Book Refinery Ltd
www.thebookrefinery.com